Specials!

Product design

John Walker and Katy Robinson

Acknowledgements

© 2009 Folens Limited, on behalf of the authors.

United Kingdom: Folens Publishers, Waterslade House, Thame Road, Haddenham, Buckinghamshire, HP17 8NT.
Email: folens@folens.com Website: www.folens.com

Ireland: Folens Publishers, Greenhills Road, Tallaght, Dublin 24.
Email: info@folens.ie Website: www.folens.ie

Commissioning editor: Paul Naish

Editor: Cathy Hurren

Text design and layout: Planman

Illustrator: Lee Nicholls/www.hardwickstudios.com; Julian Baker of JB Illustrations p41 (top right, bottom right)

Cover design: Holbrook Design

Cover image ©iStockphoto.com/flyfloor

The websites recommended in this publication were correct at the time of going to press, however, websites may have been removed or web addresses changed since that time. Folens has made every attempt to suggest websites that are reliable and appropriate for student's use. It is not unknown for unscrupulous individuals to put unsuitable material on websites that may be accessed by students. Teachers should check all websites before allowing students to access them. Folens is not responsible for the content of external websites.

For general spellings Folens adheres to the *Oxford Dictionary of English*, Second Edition (Revised), 2005.

First published 2009 by Folens Limited.

Every effort has been made to contact copyright holders of material used in this publication. If any copyright holder has been overlooked, we will be pleased to make any necessary arrangements.

British Library Cataloguing in Publication Data. A catalogue record for this publication is available from the British Library.

ISBN: 978-1-85008-465-5

Folens code FD4655

Contents

Introduction — 4

Design: past, present and future — 5
Phones through the years — 6
Which came first? — 7
How designs change — 8
Good designs versus bad designs — 9
The future — 10

Generating ideas — 11
Using visual influences — 12
Starting from scribbles — 13
Mixing up words — 14
The world's worst — 15

Global and cultural issues of design — 16
Designing environmentally-friendly products — 17
How culture affects the design process — 18
Where does food come from? — 19
What materials are products made from? — 20
Sustainability — 21

Designing for human beings — 22
Sizes of the human body — 23
Making an ergonome — 24
Measuring up — 25
Are you sitting comfortably? — 26
On the boil — 27

Modelling — 28
Sample materials — 29
Selecting materials — 30
Plasticine™ modelling — 31
Evaluating and developing your model — 32
CAD modelling — 33

Modern materials — 34
Types of modern materials — 35
Smart materials — 36
Modelling with polymorph — 37
Even more modern materials! — 38
Designing with modern materials — 39

Industrial processes — 40
Manufacturing processes — 41
How is it made? — 42
What is it made from? — 43
Injection moulding — 44
Scales of production — 45

Designing an egg cup — 46
An egg cup design — 47
Existing egg cup designs — 48
Testing egg cups — 49
Market research — 50
Design a new egg cup — 51

Designing your own product — 52
Which design is best? — 53
Designing a new product — 54
Existing products — 55
Design your own product — 56
Chosen idea — 57

Evaluation — 58
Evaluation cube — 59
User groups — 60
Testing — 61
Self-evaluation — 62
Further development — 63

Assessment sheet — 64

Introduction

Specials! Design and Technology activities are planned for students with a reading comprehension age of seven to nine years and working at levels 1 to 3. This book is divided into activities that underpin the central concepts of product design such as ergonomics, product evaluation and looking at industrial processes. It guides students through essential processes such as generating ideas, modelling and testing when they are designing and making. Two mini projects also feature to allow students to experience the whole design and make process.

This book contains ten separate units covering the topics needed to complete the theme of the book. Each unit has one or more photocopiable Resource sheets and several Activity sheets. This allows the teacher to work in different ways. The tasks are differentiated throughout the book and offer all students the opportunity to expand their skills.

The teacher can work in different ways: each unit could be taught as one or two lessons with students working individually, in pairs or in groups. Alternatively, a single Resource sheet and the related Activity sheet(s) could be used as required. Some student pages are more challenging than others so they will need to be selected accordingly.

The Teacher's notes give guidance and are laid out as follows:

Objectives
These are the main skills or knowledge to be learnt.

Prior knowledge
This refers to the minimum skills or knowledge required by students to complete the tasks. Some Activity sheets are more challenging than others and will need to be selected accordingly.

Links
All units link to the Design and Technology National Curriculum at Key Stage 3, Scottish attainment targets and the Northern Ireland and Welsh Programmes of Study.

Background
This gives additional information for the teacher about particular aspects of the topic.

Starter activity
Since the units can be taught as a lesson, a warm-up activity focusing on an aspect of the unit is suggested.

Resource sheets and Activity sheets
The Resource sheets are used as stimulus for discussion and contain no tasks or activities. Where useful, keywords are given in the Teacher's notes and related tasks are provided on the Activity sheets. Links with other Activity sheets are sometimes indicated.

Plenary
The teacher can use the suggestions here to do additional work, recap on the main points covered, or reinforce a particular point.

Assessment sheet
At the end of the book there is an Assessment sheet focusing on student progress and learning. It can be used in different ways. A student could complete it as a self-assessment, while the teacher or support assistant also completes one on the student's progress. The two can then be compared and contrasted during a discussion. Alternatively, students could work in pairs to carry out a peer-assessment and then compare outcomes.

Look out for other titles in the Design and Technology series, including:

- Designing and making
- Food
- Food 2
- Graphic products
- Resistant materials
- Sustainable design
- Systems and control
- Textiles
- Textiles 2

Teacher's notes

Design: past, present and future

Objectives

- To understand how and why products change
- To investigate when products were designed
- To consider good and bad product design
- To develop creativity and design skills, and an ability to consider the wants and needs of consumers

Prior knowledge

Students will need to have had interaction with telephones and mobile phones. They will need to be able to evaluate different aspects of products and to consider product function and user needs.

NC links

Key concepts: 1.1 Designing and making;
1.2 Cultural understanding; 1.3 Creativity;
1.4 Critical evaluation
Key processes: a, b, h
Range and content: a, b, c, d, e
Curriculum opportunities: a, b

Northern Ireland PoS

Designing: c, e, h
Communicating: a

Scottish attainment targets

Needs and how they are met: Level C

Welsh PoS

Developing thinking
Developing communication

Background

This unit aims to help students understand that products have not always looked the way they do now and that many product designs have a history. Students are required to put these changes into context to gain a greater understanding of the reasons for design changes.

Telephones are used as an example as they are a familiar product. The design of the telephone has a very clear progression through time.

Starter activity

Use the Resource sheet, 'Phones through the years', to get students talking about what they think about each of the products, for example: which one is the oldest?, Which ones have they used?, Which ones do they like?, and so on. The images on the sheet show telephones that have been manufactured from 1920 to the present day. Clockwise from top left: 700 series telephone (1960s); 200 series telephone (1930s); a cordless phone (1980s and 1990s); a 'candlestick' phone (1920s); a Trimphone (1960s); a mobile phone (1980s).

Resource sheets and Activity sheets

The Activity sheet, 'Which came first?', can be used in conjunction with the Resource sheet, 'Phones through the ages', in order to get students to consider the aesthetics and function of products, and then use this analysis to formulate a reasoned order for their design. Students are not expected to know exact dates, but they should attempt to make well thought out estimations.

The Activity sheet, 'How designs change', allows students to identify design changes to two telephones. Students' understanding may benefit from role playing the use of the phones or watching short video clips of people using them.

The Activity sheet, 'Good designs versus bad designs', helps students to realize that not all designs are necessarily good. The bad designs used in this Activity sheet all exist from patents that have been filed in the UK and the USA.

The Activity sheet, 'The future', encourages students to consider the future of mobile phone design and function. It would be beneficial for students to have a product to handle such as an old display model from a mobile phone shop. The aim of this activity is to get them to use their knowledge as a springboard for their imagination when creating a future product.

Plenary

Students could develop the 'past, present and future' idea by choosing another product and collecting images of it through time and consider how it could look in the future.

Students could also consider other good or bad product designs by collecting a range of product images explaining the good and bad points of the design. They could even create their own design 'cool wall' by placing product design images on a wall display on a scale ranging from 'seriously uncool' to 'sub-zero'.

Phones through the years

Activity sheet – Design: past, present and future

Which came first?

☞ 1 Study the Resource sheet, 'Phones through the years'. These telephones were designed from 1920 to the present day.

☞ 2 In the table below, draw three of the phones from the Resource sheet, 'Phones through the years', starting with the oldest.

Telephone	What decade was it designed in?

☞ 3 Complete the table by guessing what decade each telephone was designed in.

Activity sheet – Design: past, present and future

How designs change

☞ 1 Choose two of the telephones from the Resource sheet, 'Phones through the years'. Cut them out and stick them into the boxes below.

Telephone 1	Telephone 2

☞ 2 Answer the following questions about the telephones you have chosen.

a How do you dial the numbers?

Telephone 1	
Telephone 2	

b Can you easily walk around with it?

Telephone 1	
Telephone 2	

c Can you see any differences or good features of the telephones?

Telephone 1	
Telephone 2	

☞ 3 In a small group, discuss why you think there are differences or why changes were made.

Activity sheet – Design: past, present and future

Good designs versus bad designs

Some designs work well, but some are not so successful. It will help you with your own designing if you work out what is good or bad about a design. The table below gives some examples of bad designs that actually exist!

☞ 1 Think about how well each of the following products work. Give each design a mark out of ten for the categories provided in the chart below.

Bad designs	What it does	How well does it do its job?	How useful is it?	Does it look nice?	How safe is it?
Zip-together trousers	It lets you choose two halves of different trousers to zip together.	/10	/10	/10	/10
Motorized ice cream cone	It rotates the ice cream so you only need to stick your tongue out!	/10	/10	/10	/10
Round chess board	It lets you play chess on a circular board rather than a square one.	/10	/10	/10	/10
Car umbrella	It keeps the sun and rain off your car.	/10	/10	/10	/10

☞ 2 Which one is the worst design? Why? Discuss your ideas with a partner and decide how you could improve the products to make them better.

Activity sheet – Design: past, present and future

The future

Telephone design changes all the time. Every year new models are launched that can perform new functions or that contain new features.

☞ 1 Use a current mobile phone as an example to answer the following questions.

a What can it do? _____

_____

_____

b What special features and gadgets does it have? _____

_____

_____

c What makes it easy to use and understand? _____

_____

☞ 2 Imagine a mobile phone in ten years time and answer the following questions.

a What can it do? _____

_____

_____

b What special features and gadgets does it have? _____

_____

_____

c What makes it easy to use and understand? _____

_____

_____

☞ 3 On a separate piece of paper use your ideas from Task 2 to draw a mobile phone of the future. Add labels to your diagram to explain your design.

Teacher's notes

Generating ideas

Objectives

- To understand that different starting points and influences can be used to help generate design ideas
- To understand that all design ideas have merit, no matter how silly they seem initially
- To expand the range and direction of creative thinking and problem-solving skills

Prior knowledge

Students should have undertaken basic design tasks before. They will also need to be able to create basic drawings of their concepts.

NC links

Key concepts: 1.1 Designing and making; 1.3 Creativity
Key processes: a, b
Range and content: a
Curriculum opportunities: b

Northern Ireland PoS

Designing: c, e, f, h
Communicating: a

Scottish attainment targets

Needs and how they are met: Level B

Welsh PoS

Developing thinking
Developing communication

Background

The emphasis of this unit is to encourage students to develop their ability to generate creative solutions to design briefs. Many will find this challenging so it is essential that you foster a secure environment for them to express their ideas. When generating initial ideas anything goes, no matter how seemingly daft! Initial thoughts often spark even more creative solutions so there must be no right or wrong ideas. The sheets in this unit give very open-ended activities which can be used on their own or the processes applied to other design problems.

Starter activity

Any activity that sparks off creative thought is good. For example, hold up a selection of abstract objects, such as a piece of tubing or an offcut of foam, and ask students to think of as many uses for them as possible.

Resource sheets and Activity sheets

The Activity sheet, 'Using visual influences', requires students to study everyday objects to draw out their key design properties, such as shape, colour and texture. Students are then encouraged to consider these key design properties when redesigning an everyday object. This activity can be expanded by asking students to collect other images and keywords as starting points.

Students will often be encouraged to think of what a product is and what it does before they design it. The Activity sheet, 'Starting from scribbles', turns this around and puts form before function. By randomly scribbling, students will generate random, free-flowing shapes. They can then apply decision-making skills to select the most appropriate shapes. Once students understand this technique it may be beneficial for them to work on a large sheet of plain paper, away from the confines of a box.

Students may find the prospect of using words as a design starting point slightly daunting. By turning it into more of a game using the Activity sheet, 'Mixing up words', students are encouraged to embrace the element of chance. This activity works well as both an individual activity and a group activity, with one person reading the chosen cards out. For longevity this sheet can be photocopied onto card. New sets of describing words can be developed for each design situation.

Designing can often be very goal-driven, with pressure on students to come up with viable solutions every time. The Activity sheet, 'The world's worst', encourages students to come up with the world's worst design of something to add an element of fun to the process and take away the fear of failure. Identifying key faults can also be new avenues for students to explore when developing better solutions to other problems. Bad design ideas can be explored further by looking into Chindōgu, the Japanese art of inventing useless products to solve specific problems!

Plenary

Often, the best way to conclude a generating ideas session is to celebrate students' creativity and success as a group by getting each student to show and briefly talk about their best idea. Further activities on generating ideas can be found in the *Designing and making* title in this series.

Activity sheet – Generating ideas

Using visual influences

It can often be hard to come up with design ideas so pictures can be used to help you.

☞ Study the pictures below and think about what is visually special about each one. Use the word bank as a starting point to help you with ideas.

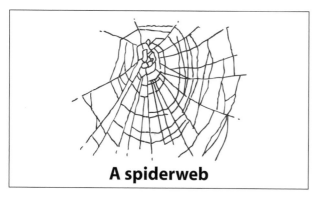

A spiderweb

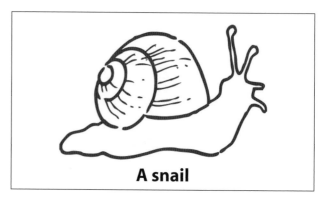

A snail

A waterfall

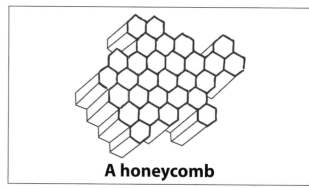

A honeycomb

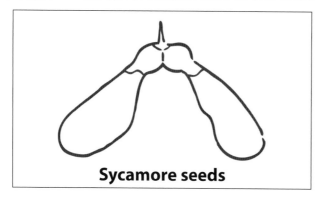

Sycamore seeds

A kangaroo

Word bank

- Soft
- Shell
- Spinning
- Flow
- Pouch

- Threads
- Fur
- Jump
- Spiral
- Seed

- Water
- Structure
- Net
- Bounce

- Strong
- Hexagon
- Slimy
- Delicate

Activity sheet – Generating ideas

Starting from scribbles

When you are stuck for ideas you can often use scribbles and shapes to help you start your design.

 1 In the box below, next to the example given, draw your own scribble.

 2 Colour in two or three shapes in your scribble and redraw them in the empty box below.

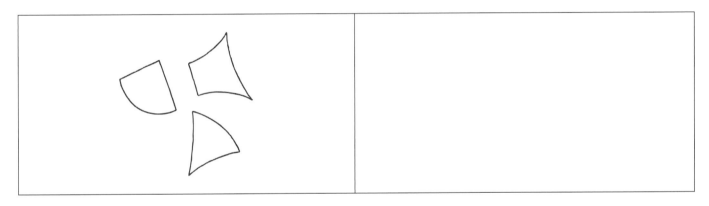

 3 Using the two or three shapes you have redrawn, think about what they could be turned into. (You could take bits away, add bits or change the shapes slightly.) Draw your ideas in the empty box below.

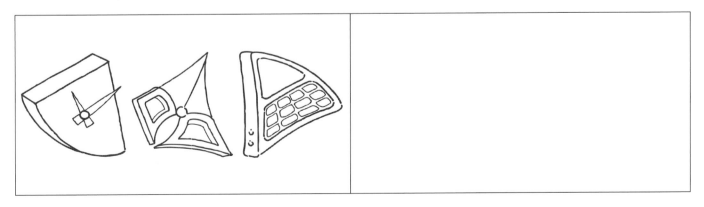

 4 Use the shapes of everyday objects to help inspire design ideas.

Activity sheet – Generating ideas

Mixing up words

As well as pictures you can also use words to help come up with design ideas. In this activity you are going to use words to help you design a new toy for young children.

☞ 1 Cut out the word cards below. Place them face down on a table and mix them up.

Rainbow	Shine	Glow	Clear
Soft	Feel	Puzzle	Build
Sort	Wobble	Bounce	Light
Heavy	Wooden	Plastic	Imagine

☞ 2 Turn over two of the word cards and write your selections in the boxes below.

Word 1:	Word 2:

☞ 3 On a separate piece of paper, use the two words you have selected to help you design an idea for a new toy for young children. An example has been given below to help you.

Word 1: *Build*
Word 2: *Rainbow*

A stacking toy made from colourful plastic that children can build up to make a rainbow.

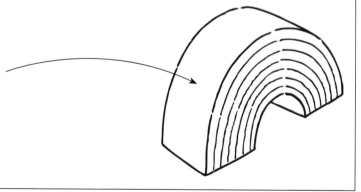

Activity sheet – Generating ideas

The world's worst

Not all designs are good designs, but this not always a bad thing! By looking at a very bad design you can see new ways to make it better.

☞ 1 In the table below there are examples of some everyday objects. Sketch the world's worst design for each one and explain what the problems are. To start you off, the problems for the first object have already been listed.

Product	The world's worst design	Problems include...
Umbrella		• Doesn't keep the user dry • Is too heavy to hold • It collapses shut
Bed		
Plate		
Letterbox		

☞ 2 For each of the ideas above, think about how you could improve each design. Note down your ideas in your workbook.

☞ 3 Think of two other objects. Draw the world's worst designs for both of them on a separate piece of paper. Remember to explain the problems of each design.

Product design

Teacher's notes

Global and cultural issues of design

Objectives

- To think about global and cultural issues of design and how this affects the user
- To consider where materials come from
- To identity how environmentally-friendly products are and what happens to them at the end of their life cycle

Prior knowledge

Students need to understand what is meant by the 3Rs (reduce, reuse and recycle) and how these affect the products that we use.

NC links

Key concepts: 1.1 Designing and making;
1.4 Critical evaluation
Key processes: d
Range and content: a, c, d, e, l
Curriculum opportunities: a, b

Northern Ireland PoS

Designing: g

Scottish attainment targets

Resources and how they are managed: Level C
Developing information attitudes: Social and environmental responsibility

Welsh PoS

Skills: Designing: 8

Background

This unit will enable students to explore different issues that affect the world we live in, in order to develop their awareness of different users. This ranges from the environmental effects of old products, an understanding of other cultures and where materials come from. This unit explores the needs of different cultures through the identification of what we call 'everyday items' and how other cultures could see them as luxury items.

Starter activity

Discuss with students their knowledge of the 3Rs, how often they themselves recycle, what sort of products could be reused and the amount of packaging that's used. Ask students what they consider to be essential products that they cannot live without but that they might be taking for granted, such as products that developing countries may not have access to.

Resource sheets and Activity sheets

The Resource sheet, 'Designing environmentally-friendly products', should be used to prompt students to think about the environmental implications of a product when designing. This Resource sheet can then be used in relation to any of the Activity sheets in this unit.

The Activity sheet, 'How culture affects the design process', asks students to study two houses from different parts of the world. The houses have been designed using local materials and to meet the needs of those living in a particular country. Students should be encouraged to consider how effective each house design is, their differences and similarities and why that is.

Using the Activity sheet, 'Where does food come from?', students will look at the packaging of their favourite food item or some general food packaging in relation to where the food was produced and if the packaging can be recycled.

The Activity sheet, 'What are product materials made from?', requires students to consider a range of products, where the materials they are made of have come from and whether the material is renewable or not.

Using the Activity sheet, 'Sustainability', students are to investigate the sustainability of products they themselves or their family purchase and replace. Students are then encouraged to design a sculpture using old electrical products to advertise and encourage recycling.

Plenary

Ask students to talk about items that they themselves have recycled, and how, and in what ways, other items could be recycled. Students could also talk about unsustainable materials and what will happen once they are no longer available.

Designing environmentally-friendly products

To help you design environmentally-friendly products use the spinner below. Cut it out, stick it onto card and insert a pencil into the centre. Spin the spinner twice and consider the two points it lands on. How might you design your product?

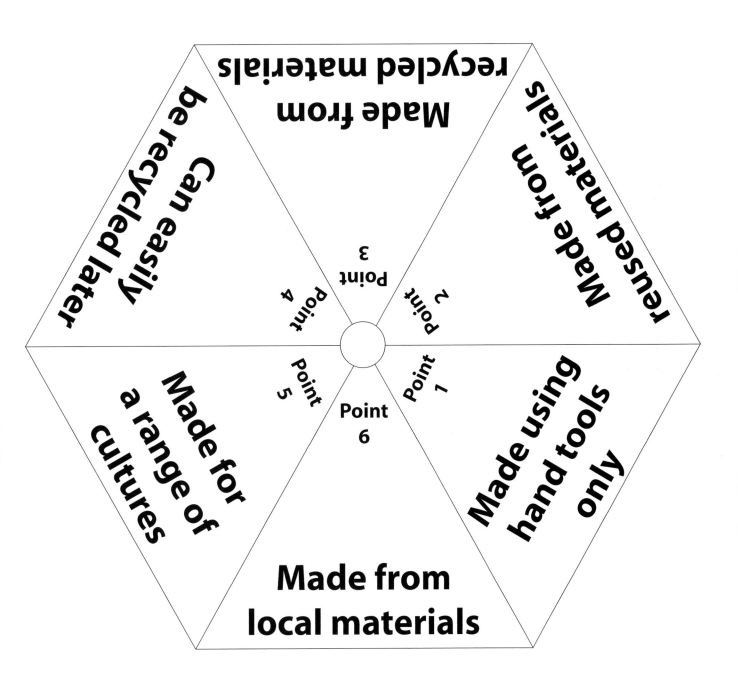

Activity sheet – Global and cultural issues of design

How culture affects the design process

The two houses below are from different parts of the world. They have been designed using local materials and to meet the needs of those living in a particular country.

☞ Study the two houses and answer the questions below in the boxes provided.

a What are the differences between the two houses?

b What are the similarities between the two houses?

c How have the houses been designed to meet the needs of the people that live in them?

Where does food come from?

Activity sheet – Global and cultural issues of design

☞ 1 Either draw a picture of a snack wrapper, place a photo of the packaging or stick the actual wrapper in the large box below.

☞ 2 Answer the following questions about the snack wrapper in the spaces provided.

Do you think this product needs this packaging? Why?

Does the product actually fill the packaging?

Can the packaging be recycled?

Where was the product made or grown?

What is the packaging made from?

What kind of carrier bag did you use when you bought the snack?

Activity sheet – Global and cultural issues of design

What materials are products made from?

☞ 1 Draw an arrow from each of the following products on the left-hand side to match them to the raw material they are made from shown on the right-hand side. The first one has been done to help you.

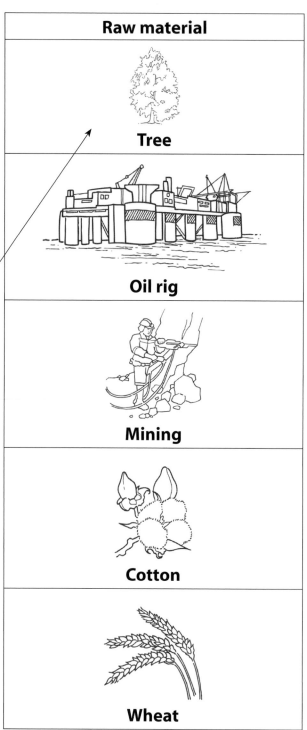

☞ 2 Which of the products are made from renewable resources? Discuss with a partner which products you use. Which are made from renewable resources? Which are not?

Product design

Activity sheet – Global and cultural issues of design

Sustainability

Every year people in Britain throw away over one million tonnes of electrical waste.
Sustainability is about living within our means and using the resources we have wisely.

☞ 1 In the box below list all of the new electrical products that you or your family have
bought so far this year.

```
[blank box]
```

☞ 2 In the box below write down if the new products were bought to replace old
products. Note down if the old ones were thrown away.

```
[blank box]
```

☞ 3 In the box below design a sculpture made from old electrical products, such as
televisions, washing machines, and so on, to encourage or advertise recycling.

```
[blank box]
```

Teacher's notes

Designing for human beings

Objectives

- To understand that the size and shape of the human body has to be considered when designing products
- To develop awareness of the design needs of people of different proportions
- To practice skills in taking measurements and working in units of measurement

Prior knowledge

Students should be able to generate ideas based on their experience of the world around them, their interaction with everyday objects and be able to reflect upon these interactions. Students should be able to take and use basic units of measurement.

NC links

Key concepts: 1.1 Designing and making
Key processes: d
Range and content: a, b, c, e
Curriculum opportunities: a, b

Northern Ireland PoS

Designing: b, c, e, g, h
Communicating: a, b

Scottish attainment targets

Needs and how they are met: Level C

Welsh PoS

Developing thinking; Developing communication; Developing number; Personal and social

Background

This unit introduces human factors design: designing products for human beings. This is a simplified name for ergonomics and anthropometrics – taking into consideration how people interact with products and how they fit both the human body and a person's life.

Starter activity

Ask students to look around the classroom and think about what items were designed taking into account the size and shape of human beings as well as their personal needs. Students should feed back their ideas to the class and compile a list of these items on the whiteboard. Ask students to think about what specific measurements or requirements were considered when the items were designed; these should then be written alongside the items listed on the whiteboard.

Resource sheets and Activity sheets

The Resource sheet, 'Sizes of the human body', contains basic anthropometric data: measurements of below average height, average height and above average height people which can be useful when designing products. This sheet can be used in conjunction with most of the Activity sheets in this unit, but also as a stand alone resource for extension projects.

The Activity sheet, 'Making an ergonome', is a good introduction to this topic. By making the scale model, students will have a resource that they can handle and manipulate, giving them a framework to design around. This Activity sheet works best if photocopied onto card prior to being cut up.

The Activity sheet, 'Measuring up', introduces students to the concept of anthropometrics by getting them to consider designs and the measurements used to create them. This activity could be extended through the use of the Resource sheet, 'Sizes of the human body', by asking students to design specific objects to fit specific people.

The Activity sheet, 'Are you sitting comfortably?', aims to get students to consider the design of an everyday object. Students will need access to a tape measure or metre ruler and a chair in order to take some basic measurements.

Using the Activity sheet, 'On the boil', students are to think about other users of everyday products and their specific ergonomic needs. The focus is on identifying very definite design needs while still allowing students the freedom to think up imaginative solutions to these needs.

Plenary

Students could create a full-scale ergonome by drawing around the outline of a volunteer onto thick card and then fixing it together in the same way as the scale model with paper fasteners. This could then be used to create and test some larger designs in profile, for example, a car seat and steering wheel or a computer desk and chair.

Resource sheet – Designing for human beings

Sizes of the human body

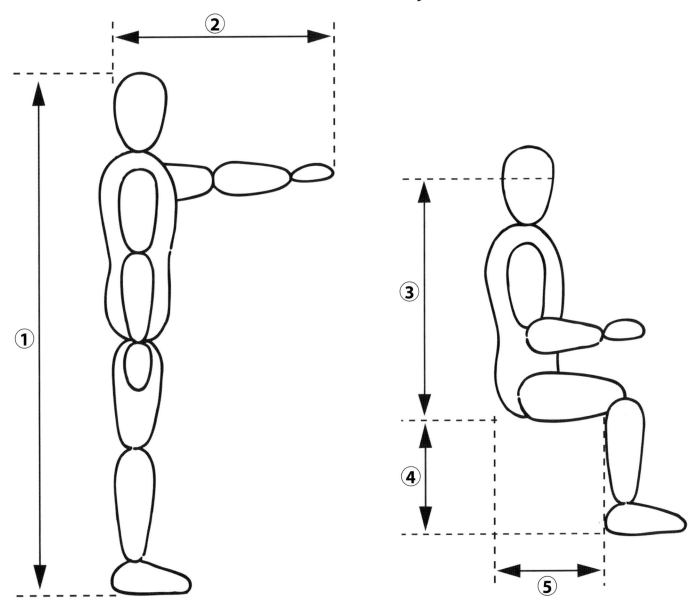

The following table gives below average height, average height and above average height measurements for an adult male.

Measurement	Below average height	Average height	Above average height
1 Overall height	1505mm	1675mm	1855mm
2 Forward reach	650mm	743mm	835mm
3 Sitting eye level	685mm	765mm	845mm
4 Seat height	355mm	420mm	490mm
5 Seat depth	435mm	488mm	550mm

Activity sheet – Designing for human beings

Making an ergonome

An ergonome (also known as a moveable anthropometric figure) is a scale model of a human being. It can be moved into different positions to help you design products that fit the human body. You can use it to make your designs the correct size and shape.

☞ 1 Cut out the pieces of the ergonome below.

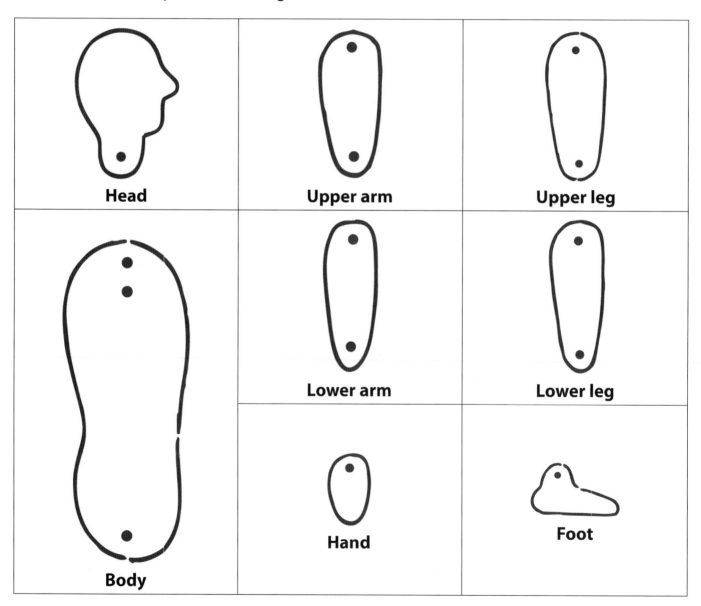

☞ 2 Carefully make a small hole where the black dots are and join the pieces together using paper fasteners.

☞ 3 Use your ergonome to help you design some furniture such as a chair. Sit it down and draw around its outline.

☞ 4 With a partner, discuss what other furniture could be designed using the ergonome.

Product design

Activity sheet – Designing for human beings

Measuring up

People come in all shapes and sizes. When designing a product you must remember that many different people will use it. Using measurements when designing is called anthropometrics.

☞ 1 Look at the furniture and equipment in your classroom. Think about whether a designer used measurements of the human body when designing it.

☞ 2 In the first column of the table below list three objects you think used measurements of the human body in their design. An example has been given to help you.

☞ 3 In the second column of the table describe the measurements that would have been considered for each object. An example has been given to help you.

Object	Measurements used
The whiteboard	• *How high the teacher can reach* • *The teacher's eye level*

☞ 4 Complete the following table by taking the measurements of people in your class.

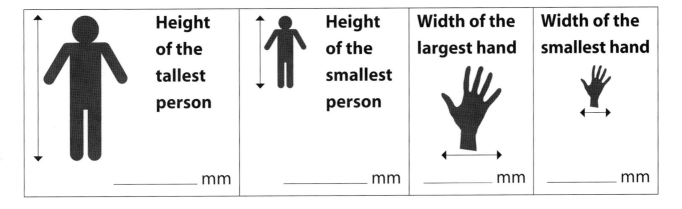

Activity sheet – Designing for human beings

Are you sitting comfortably?

You probably spend many hours every day sat on a chair. Their design is important so that you can be comfortable.

☞ 1 Stand up and look at the chair you were sitting on.

☞ 2 Using the diagram below as a guide, use a tape measure or a metre ruler to measure your chair. Write the measurements in the boxes provided.

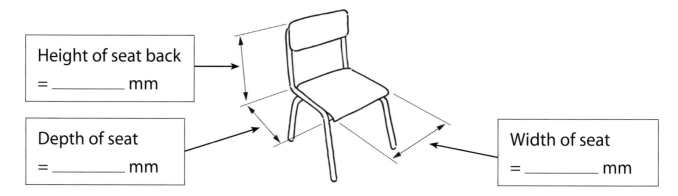

Height of seat back
= _____ mm

Depth of seat
= _____ mm

Width of seat
= _____ mm

☞ 3 Now sit back on your chair. Think about its design and answer the following questions in the spaces provided.

a Does it fit your body?

b Do your feet touch the ground?

c Does your bottom fit on the seat?

d Are there any measurements you might change to make it fit your body better?

☞ 4 On a separate piece of paper, redesign your chair to fit your body better.

Activity sheet – Designing for human beings

On the boil

Every well-designed product must be comfortable, safe and easy to use. This is called ergonomics.

☞ 1 Study the picture of a kettle. Think about how you might use it to make a hot drink. You would probably find it quite easy to use whilst other people may not.

☞ 2 Think about an elderly person who may not be able to use their hands very well or who cannot see very well. In the box below draw a picture of how you could improve the kettle design to make it easier for an elderly person to use.

☞ 3 Write down what improvements you have made: _____

_____

_____

_____

_____

_____

_____

_____

☞ 4 On a separate piece of paper, design a kettle that would be safe to use in a house full of young children. Remember to add notes to your design to explain it.

Product design

Teacher's notes

Modelling

Objectives

- To be able to find information about a product's materials
- To carry out research on a chosen product
- To design/redesign a new product (for example, an egg cup, a computer mouse, or a mobile phone) taking into account the materials it is made of

Prior knowledge

Students should have first completed research into a chosen product by creating a mood board or by evaluating existing products.

NC links

Key concepts: 1.1 Designing and making;
1.3 Creativity
Key processes: a, b
Range and content: a, b
Curriculum opportunities: a, b, c

Northern Ireland PoS

Designing: e

Scottish attainment targets

Resources and how they are managed: Level B
Skills in designing and making: carrying out tasks:
Level B

Welsh PoS

Skills: Designing: 7

Background

This unit will enable students to explore a range of different ways of modelling and help them visualize their ideas, allowing them to select the best materials. Students will learn that modelling can be carried out using materials such as Plasticine™ or CAD software such as Google's SketchUp (available free online).

Starter activity

Students should collect a range of different materials and glue them onto the Resource sheet, 'Sample materials'. This will give them a chance to handle and discuss different materials and refer back to them during the unit.

Resource sheets and Activity sheets

Using the Resource sheet, 'Sample materials', as part of the starter activity will enable students to handle different materials and refer back to them when selecting the best materials for products they make.

The Activity sheet, 'Selecting materials', encourages students to consider a range of different materials for a product and explain why the materials they have chosen are the most appropriate.

The Activity sheet, 'Plasticine™ modelling', allows students to draw out four different ideas for their product. They will then create their favourite out of Plasticine™. There is space for a photo of the model to be glued onto the page so a record of the Plasticine™ model can be kept.

Using the Activity sheet, 'Evaluating and developing your model', students are to evaluate their Plasticine™ model and consider the materials they would use to build it.

The Activity sheet, 'CAD modelling', requires students to create a 3-D model of their work using CAD software such as ProDesktop, ProENGINEER, SolidWorks or Google's SketchUp. Using CAD software will mean that students can quickly make changes to their work.

Plenary

Ask students to explain what they have found out about the design of their work and how modelling has helped them to visualize their ideas.

Resource sheet – Modelling

Sample materials

Collect samples of the following materials and attach them to the boxes below. Look at and feel each material when you start a new project. This can help you visualize the materials you are going to use.

Wood	Plastic

Fabric	Metal

Foam	Rubber

Activity sheet – Modelling

Selecting materials

☞ 1 Choose a product and look at the materials it is made of.

☞ 2 Draw the product or stick a photo of it in the middle box below.

☞ 3 Consider the materials listed below. Decide if the product would be better or worse if it was made from that material.

Mixture of materials

☐ Metal ☐ Rubber

☐ Foam ☐ Plastic

☐ Wood ☐ Fabric

Why? _____

_____

_____

The product

Wood

☐ Better?

☐ Worse?

☐ No different?

Why? _____

_____

_____

Metal

☐ Better?

☐ Worse?

☐ No different?

Why? _____

_____

_____

Plastic

☐ Better?

☐ Worse?

☐ No different?

Why? _____

_____

_____

Foam

☐ Better?

☐ Worse?

☐ No different?

Why? _____

_____

_____

Fabric

☐ Better?

☐ Worse?

☐ No different?

Why? _____

_____

_____

Rubber

☐ Better?

☐ Worse?

☐ No different?

Why? _____

_____

_____

Product design

Activity sheet – Modelling

Plasticine™ modelling

In this activity you will be using Plasticine™ to create a model of a product of your choice.

☞ 1 Sketch out four ideas for your product in the spaces below.

Idea 1	**Idea 2**

Idea 3	**Idea 4**

☞ 2 Choose the best one and make it out of Plasticine™.

☞ 3 Take a photo of your Plasticine™ model and attach it to the back of this sheet.

Activity sheet – Modelling

Evaluating and developing your model

Once you have modelled your design using Plasticine™ you will need to see if the design is as good as you expected it to be.

☞ Answer the following questions in the spaces provided to find out if your design is a good one.

1 Does your Plasticine™ model look like your design? If not, why not?

2 How do you think you could improve your model?

3 Do you need to change the size of your product? If so, why?

4 How do you think your design will appeal to people? (Think about its shape, texture, and so on.)

5 What materials would you select to make your final product and why?

Product design

Activity sheet – Modelling

CAD modelling

The use of CAD (computer-aided design) can help you and other people to quickly see what your ideas look like.

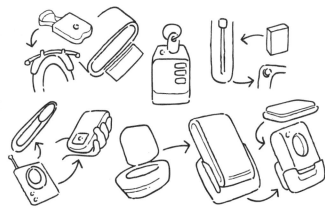

 1 Use CAD software to model your product idea.

 2 Print out your design and stick it the space below.

 3 Add notes to your design to develop your ideas.

Teacher's notes

Modern materials

Objectives

- To gain an understanding of a wide range of modern materials
- To learn about how materials can react to outside stimuli
- To investigate how these materials can be applied to product designs

Prior knowledge

Students will need an awareness of the basic materials used in design and technology, and a basic understanding of properties.

NC links

Key concepts: 1.1 Designing and making
Key processes: a, c
Range and content: a, e, l
Curriculum opportunities: a, b

Northern Ireland PoS

Designing: b, e, f
Communicating: a, b

Scottish attainment targets

Needs and how they are met: Level B
Processes and how they are applied: Level A

Welsh PoS

Developing thinking; Developing communication; Personal and social

Background

Scientists and technologists develop new materials all the time: these new materials can offer innovative applications that can aid new product development. A modern material is classed as something which has been developed over recent years, different from the usual wood, metal and plastic materials. A subset of modern materials are smart materials. Smart materials can change their properties in a range of ways when different stimuli are applied. For example, some will change colour when heat is applied whilst others will change size if an electrical current is applied.

Starter activity

Students will ideally have access to a small collection of modern materials such as polymorph, thermochromic and photochromic materials or shape memory alloys – these can be obtained from design and technology suppliers. It would be good for students to handle these materials and to experience the effects of various stimuli on them such as placing their hand on thermochromic film until it changes colour. A discussion can then be started as to what uses they could have on various designs.

Resource sheets and Activity sheets

The Resource sheet, 'Types of modern materials', describes four of the most common modern materials. This can be used to reinforce the starter activity and links to all of the Activity sheets in this unit.

The Activity sheet, 'Smart materials', is designed to get students to think about how materials behave and the various ways in which they are used. Students could use the Resource sheet, 'Types of modern materials', to identify the materials on this Activity sheet.

The Activity sheet, 'Modelling with polymorph', outlines a simple practical task that can be undertaken using polymorph to mould an ergonomic pencil grip. Although it can appear expensive to buy, polymorph can be warmed and used over and over again. Students will need access to a beaker, a source of hot water, spoons and pencils. Students must NOT wrap or mould the polymorph around a body part, as it hardens.

The Activity sheet, 'Even more modern materials!', introduces students to more modern materials and asks them to consider their properties. Students are then encouraged to design new applications for them.

The Activity sheet, 'Designing with modern materials', aims to bring together the knowledge that students have gained in the previous Activity sheets and to enable them to start applying it to real world problems. Students may need to discuss their design briefs first, but once they have the basic material needed they should be encouraged to let their imaginations run riot!

Plenary

Students could be encouraged to start thinking about where modern materials might be in 15 years time: what they might do, what properties they might have and what design problems they could solve. The national press often carry articles about new material developments which students could discuss as they arise to reinforce prior learning.

Resource sheet – Modern materials

Types of modern materials

Although you often work with wood, metal or plastic there are many more modern materials you can use. A lot of these materials have been developed quite recently. These are called smart materials. Smart materials have one or more properties that mean it can change its shape when something is applied to it such as light, heat, electricity or water.

Polymorph is a plastic, but it is different to other types of plastic. It comes in granules, which can be heated with hot water or a hairdryer. Once heated it can be moulded into any shape you like.	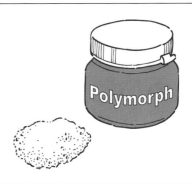
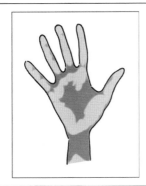	Thermochromic materials change colour with temperature. They often come in the form of a film.
Photochromic materials change colour with light, either daylight or the dark. This material is used in reflection lenses.	
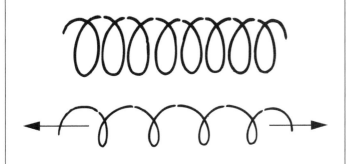	Shape memory alloys are made from a mixture of metals. They can be stretched out of shape but when heated they return to their original shape. They can be heated by passing electricity through them.

Product design

Activity sheet – Modern materials

Smart materials

☞ 1 Cut out the following picture cards.

A thermometer showing your
temperature in colour.

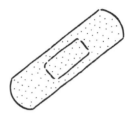

A sticking plaster that tells you when you
have been in the sun too long.

Bendable frames for glasses.

A fire exit sign that glows in the dark.

A mug that changes colour when
a hot drink is poured into it.

A rubber duck that changes
colour in the bath.

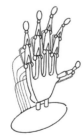

A model hand with moving fingers.

Lenses that go dark in sunlight.

☞ 2 Using the Resource sheet, 'Types of modern materials', sort the picture cards into
the different types of smart materials.

Product design

Activity sheet – Modern materials

Modelling with polymorph

Polymorph is plastic that can be easily shaped using hot water. Remember, **do not** wrap polymorph around your hands or body because it harderns.

☞ 1 Carefully follow the instructions below to create a new grip for your pencil.

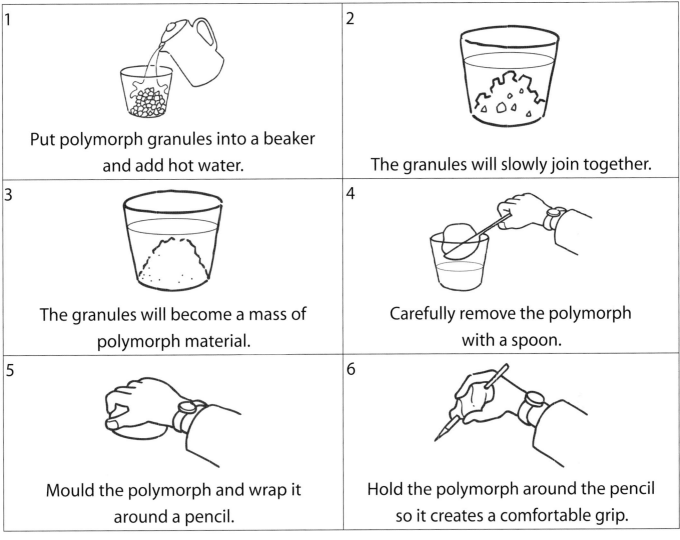

1	2
Put polymorph granules into a beaker and add hot water.	The granules will slowly join together.
3	4
The granules will become a mass of polymorph material.	Carefully remove the polymorph with a spoon.
5	6
Mould the polymorph and wrap it around a pencil.	Hold the polymorph around the pencil so it creates a comfortable grip.

☞ 2 Stick a photo or draw a picture of your pencil grip design in the box below.

Even more modern materials!

New materials are being developed all the time. Good designers always try to find new uses for these materials.

For example, there are lids on food packaging that change colour to tell you when it is cool enough to eat or drink.

There are fabrics which, when the person wearing them moves, change pattern.

There is a gel called d3o that when something hits it, it hardens. This is being used for products such as helmets and knee-pads.

☞   1 Think about how each of these materials work.

☞   2 In the space below write down your ideas about other ways in which these materials could be used.

☞   3 Choose one of your ideas and sketch it out in the box below.

Designing with modern materials

☞ Use what you have learnt about smart materials to solve the following problems. Write or draw your answers in the boxes provided.

a How could a parent know when their child's bathwater is the correct temperature?

b How could an elderly, hard of hearing person know when their kettle has boiled?

c How could you create a handle for carrying bags that fits your own hand?

Teacher's notes

Industrial processes

Objectives

- To gain an insight into how products are manufactured outside of the school environment and to identify which products use these processes
- To be able to identify and classify products by the materials they are made from
- To gain knowledge about the injection moulding process
- To learn the difference between one-off, batch and mass production

Prior knowledge

Students must be able to recognize the basic categories of materials and what they are made from.

NC links

Key concepts: 1.1 Designing and making
Key processes: f
Range and content: a, e, j
Curriculum opportunities: a, b

Northern Ireland PoS

Communicating: a, b
Manufacturing: b

Scottish attainment targets

Processes and how they applied: Level A

Welsh PoS

Developing thinking
Developing communication

Background

The world of industry and manufacturing products commercially is very different from creating products in a school environment. This unit aims to give students a basic awareness and introduction to a number of aspects of industrial manufacturing processes.

Starter activity

To introduce students to the concept of industrial manufacturing, gather a selection of products together, including mass-produced and one-off pieces made from wood, metal or plastic. Encourage students to discuss where they think the products are made and how they think they are manufactured. If possible, disassemble a few products to create a discussion point for students to investigate how the product might be manufactured.

Resource sheets and Activity sheets

The Resource sheet, 'Manufacturing processes', identifies some key processes used in industry, however, this is by no means a complete list. This Resource sheet could be supplemented by showing students video footage from the Internet to show the processes in action.

The Activity sheet, 'How is it made?', asks students to consider how various products are manufactured based on the information given on the Resource sheet, 'Manufacturing processes'.

The Activity sheet, 'What is it made from?', brings in kinesthetic learning as students need to identify and categorize a number of different products. Students should conclude that products using a mix of materials were the easiest to find because different materials are suitable for different jobs due to their properties.

The Activity sheet, 'Injection moulding', asks students to assemble a basic version of an injection moulding machine, label its parts and identify the job each part carries out.

The Activity sheet, 'Scales of production', introduces students to the quantities in which products are manufactured and the terms used to categorize them. Some products might become a discussion point as they may fall into more than one category. Students might find that the majority of products are mass-produced these days.

Plenary

Students could conduct a small research task to investigate one process in more detail. Another way for students to get a greater insight into manufacturing is to take them on a factory visit.

Manufacturing processes

Blow moulding is used to make plastic products with thin walls. These products usually have a neck or narrow opening.

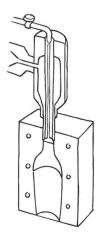

Casting is where a melted material is poured into a mould and allowed to set. It can be used to make products from metal, concrete or resin.

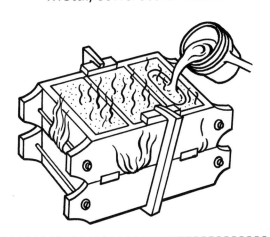

Injection moulding is used to make three dimensional (3-D) plastic products. It is good for making lots of the same product.

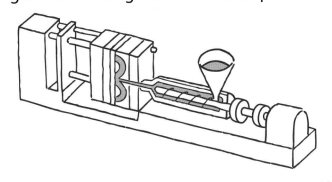

Printing is used to get pictures and words onto a material. Ink is often printed directly onto paper.

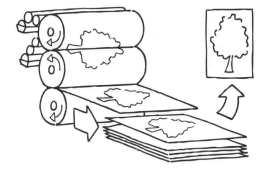

Extrusion is how you make something that is the same shape all along its length. Plastic and metal can be extruded.

Vacuum forming is where you get a thin sheet of plastic to shape around a mould.

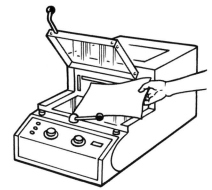

Activity sheet – Industrial processes

How is it made?

☞ 1 Cut out the following picture cards and the ones from the Resource sheet, 'Manufacturing processes'.

☞ 2 Match the products from this Activity sheet to the manufacturing processes from the Resource sheet, 'Manufacturing processes'.

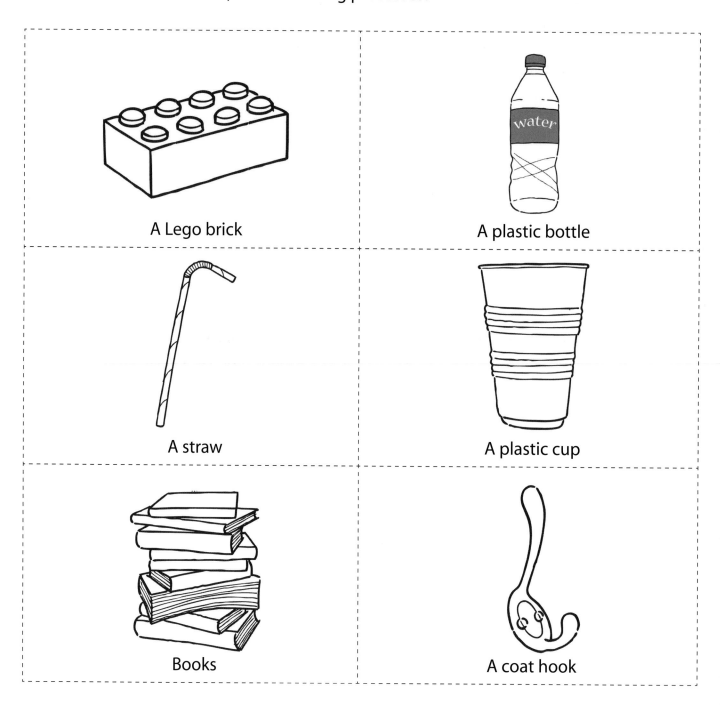

A Lego brick	A plastic bottle
A straw	A plastic cup
Books	A coat hook

☞ 3 With a partner, try to think of some more examples of products made using these processes.

Activity sheet – Industrial processes

What is it made from?

Most products are made from wood, metal or plastic. Some can be made from other materials. Sometimes they can be made from a mixture of materials.

☞ 1 Identify a range of products in your classroom and decide what they are made of. Draw them in the correct box below. Try to find at least three products for each box. An example of a metal door handle has been given to help you.

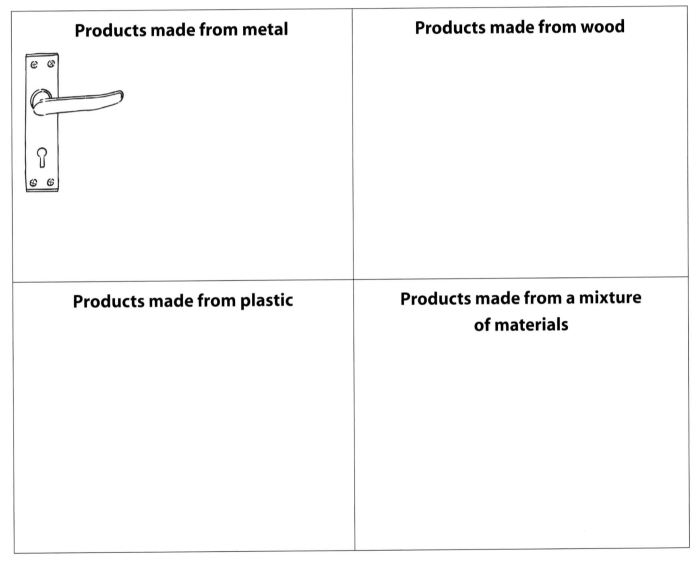

Products made from metal	Products made from wood
Products made from plastic	**Products made from a mixture of materials**

☞ 2 Which box was the easiest to find products for? Why do you think this was? Write your answers in the box below.

Injection moulding

Injection moulding is one of the most common ways of making products in a factory. Little chips of plastic are put in at one end of the machine and are forced into a mould by pressure. The plastic is allowed to cool and the finished part comes out the other end.

☞ 1 Cut out the jigsaw pieces which show the injection moulding machine process.

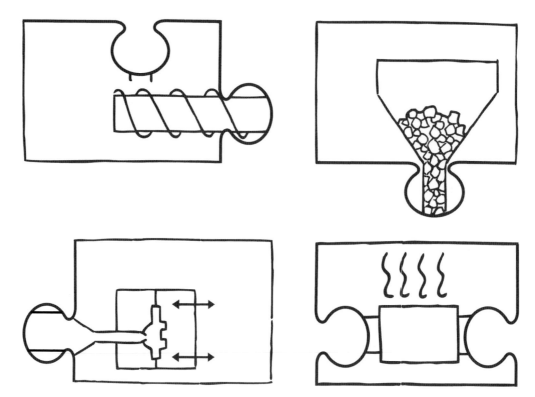

☞ 2 Complete the jigsaw by putting the pieces together and sticking them in your workbook.

☞ 3 Cut out the following labels and stick them next to the correct jigsaw piece to label the parts of the injection mould machine.

Plastic chips are placed in the hopper.	The plastic chips are heated until they have melted.
Melted plastic is injected into the mould. The mould comes apart along with the cooled, completed plastic part.	The spiral carries plastic chips along the machine.

Activity sheet – Industrial processes

Scales of production

Different products are manufactured in different quantities. For example, millions of the same toy are made at the same time whereas some pieces of furniture are only made once.

☞ 1 Place the words from the following word bank into the table where you think they belong.

Word bank

- Plastic cups
- A cruise ship
- Cars
- Rubber ducks
- An MP3 player
- A wedding dress
- Flat-pack furniture
- Loaves of bread
- The Crown jewels
- A skyscraper

One-off production Only one of the product is manufactured	
Batch production Small numbers of the same product are manufactured	
Mass production Lots of the same product is manufactured	

☞ 2 Think of other product examples and list them in the table.

Teacher's notes

Designing an egg cup

Objectives

- To be able to identify appropriate design information about egg cups
- To carry out market research on a range of different egg cup designs
- To design a new egg cup, taking into account the results of market research

Prior knowledge

Students should have a basic knowledge of the design process and the use of different materials.

NC links

Key concepts: 1.1 Designing and making
Key processes: b, d, e, f, g
Range and content: a, b, k, m
Curriculum opportunities: a, b, c

Northern Ireland PoS

Manufacturing: d

Scottish attainment targets

Skills in designing and making: preparing for tasks: Level C
Developing informed attitudes: a commitment to learning

Welsh PoS

Skills: Making 1, 2

Background

This unit will enable students to explore a range of different egg cup designs and their form and function through a number of testing methods. Students will design their own egg cup after taking into account the needs of the user. To lead this project to an outcome, students could build a model of their design by choosing from a wide range of materials such as wood and plastic or papier mâché and clay.

Starter activity

Question students about what they think the design of an egg cup should include. This could be carried out by using a selection of egg cups for the students to study, for example, an Alessi Cico or Lego egg cup design. Students could be asked to create quick sketches of egg cups and annotate their drawings to highlight the key features.

Resource sheets and Activity sheets

The Resource sheet, 'An egg cup design', prompts students to evaluate an existing egg cup design. Students can then explain what they think about the design and what materials they think an egg cup could be made from.

The Activity sheet, 'Existing egg cup designs', encourages students to consider some existing egg cups and evaluate their designs.

Using the Activity sheet, 'Testing egg cups', you (or the students) should bring in a selection of different egg cups and some chocolate eggs. Ask students to use their egg cup to hold the chocolate egg and see if they can eat it easily using the egg cup to hold the egg. When students have tested their egg cup, they need to draw a sketch of it or take a photo. They should then label key parts of the cup and say if the cup securely held the egg.

Using the Activity sheet, 'Market research', students are to write a questionnaire about egg cups using keywords. This activity could be extended by students being encouraged to display their findings as a pie chart or graph.

The Activity sheet, 'Design a new egg cup', asks students to develop their own egg cup design based on their new knowledge. Students should be encouraged to have a theme when designing their own egg cup such as sport or a cartoon character. They should annotate their designs to explain their ideas.

Plenary

Ask students to explain what they have found out about the design of egg cups. They could show what they found from their questionnaire, present their own egg cup design and explain how their research influenced their ideas.

Resource sheet – Designing an egg cup

An egg cup design

Egg cups can come in a range of different designs, but they contain some common features.

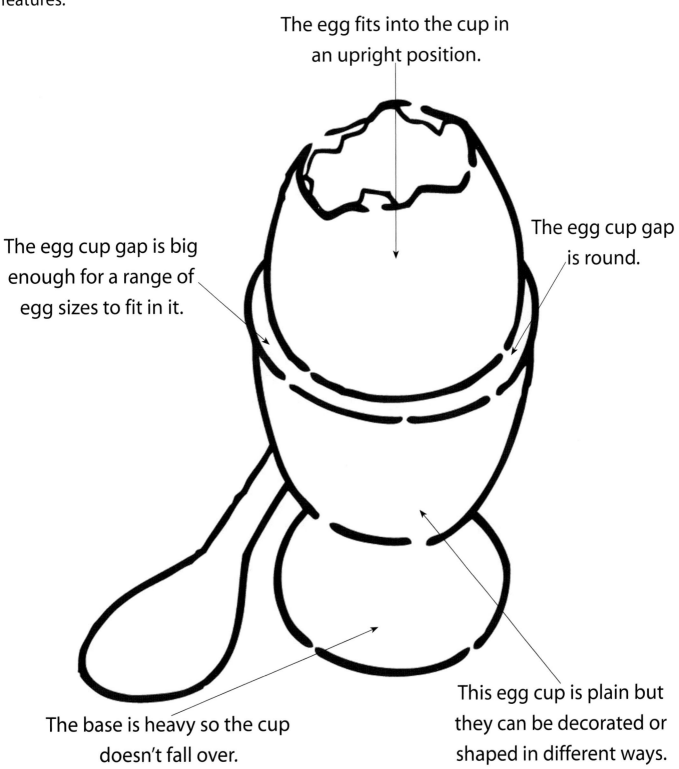

The egg fits into the cup in an upright position.

The egg cup gap is round.

The egg cup gap is big enough for a range of egg sizes to fit in it.

This egg cup is plain but they can be decorated or shaped in different ways.

The base is heavy so the cup doesn't fall over.

It would be useful to take these features into consideration when designing your own egg cup.

Activity sheet – Designing an egg cup

Existing egg cup designs

To help you understand what a product does, you can look at existing examples of it.

☞ Next to the egg cup examples below, write down what you think of each one. To help you, think about answers to the following questions:

- What do you think is good about the design?
- Do you like the design? Why?
- Would you buy this product? Why?
- How do you think the design could be improved?
- Do you think the design means that the product functions properly? Why?

　Product design

Activity sheet – Designing an egg cup

Testing egg cups

To see if something works correctly you need to test it.

☞ 1 In the box to the right, draw a picture or stick a photo of the egg cup you will be using.

☞ 2 Use the egg cup to see if you can eat an egg from it.

☞ 3 Answer the following questions about the egg cup you are using.

a Explain why it works well or doesn't work well.

b What is good about the product?

c What is bad about the product?

d What would make the product better?

Activity sheet – Designing an egg cup

Market research

To find out what people like, you need to ask them questions using a questionnaire.

☞ Write one question in each of the boxes below to find out what other people want from an egg cup. You could include questions about shape, size, colour and theme. Use the keywords box at the bottom of the page to help you.

Question 1
Question 2
Question 3
Question 4
Question 5
Question 6

Keywords

- Who
- When
- Prefer
- Theme

- Larger
- What
- Like
- Want

- Shape
- Smaller
- Why
- Need

- Enjoy
- Colour
- Where
- Dislike

- Features
- Style
- Texture
- Product

Activity sheet – Designing an egg cup

Design a new egg cup

☞ 1 In the boxes provided, draw out ideas for your new egg cup design.

☞ 2 Label each of your designs to explain them and note down what materials you would make them from. Write down what gave you the idea for each design.

Design 1

Design 2

Design 3

Design 4

Teacher's notes

Designing your own product

Objectives

- To be able to design a product using research and initial ideas to inform the final design
- To identify different ways of researching to get information

Prior knowledge

Students should have prior knowledge of materials and the design process. They should also have a basic knowledge of how to use different materials and the tools that are required to work with different materials.

NC links

Key concepts: 1.1 Designing and making
Key processes: a, b
Range and content: a, c, e
Curriculum opportunities: a, b, c

Northern Ireland PoS

Manufacturing: d

Scottish attainment targets

Needs and how they are met: Level B
Skills in designing and making: carring out tasks: Level D

Welsh PoS

Skills: Making 1, 2

Background

This unit is designed to enable students to have more creative freedom when producing designs for their own products whilst still giving them a controlled format to lay their work out in. The Activity sheets in this unit can be used for a range of different projects.

Starter activity

Discuss with students about what kind of product they would like to make. To help with inspiration, you could provide a selection of existing products for the students to test to see which ideas they like and to help them identify any improvements or modifications that they think are necessary. Students could use the existing products to help them write a list of points (a specification) that the product they are going to design must cover.

Resource sheets and Activity sheets

The Resource sheet, 'Which design is best?', demonstrates a selection of products that students could design for this unit. It could also be used as a starting point for students to discuss what they like and dislike about the products and how they think they could be improved.

The Activity sheet, 'Designing a new product', encourages students to list a number of different products they would like to design. This could then form a group discussion to decide on what product they are going to make. Students are then asked to explain what the product must do in order to form a brief and list points that the design must cover when completed in order to form a specification.

Students should use the Activity sheet, 'Existing products', to analyze existing solutions. These solutions could have been identified by an individual or as a group.

The Activity sheet, 'Design your own product', allows students to create a range of different initial ideas before choosing a final idea.

Students should use the Activity sheet, 'Chosen idea', to flesh out their chosen idea on a larger scale by labelling key parts, deciding on materials, joining techniques, and so on.

Plenary

Students could evaluate their design idea by explaining what they think is good or bad about it and how it could be improved. Students could also present their questionnaire findings and explain how research has helped their design.

Product design

Resource sheet – Designing your own product

Which design is best?

Below is a selection of different products.

☞ Study each item carefully. Discuss the designs with a partner or in a small group. Which do you like best and why? What materials do you think they are made of? How do you think they could be improved?

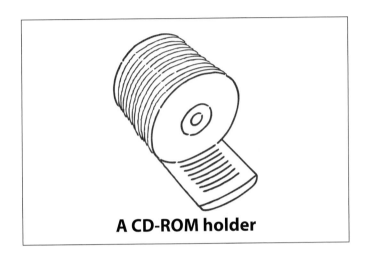

A CD-ROM holder

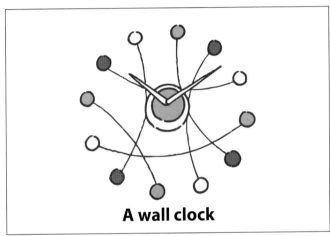

A wall clock

A desk tidy

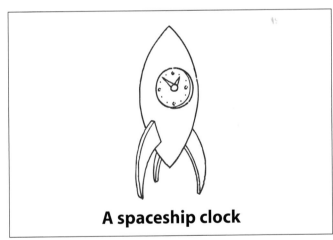

A spaceship clock

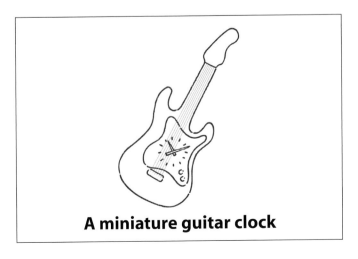

A miniature guitar clock

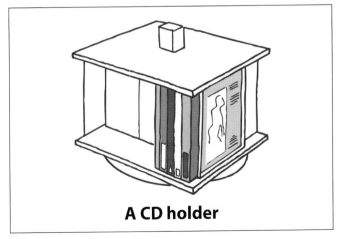

A CD holder

Activity sheet – Designing your own product

Designing a new product

☞ 1 In the space below, list five new products that you would like to design. This could range from ideas such as a desk tidy to a mobile phone holder.

1 _____

2 _____

3 _____

4 _____

5 _____

☞ 2 Complete the following table with details of the product you are going to make, such as its colour, shape, and so on. This is called a **brief**.

I am going to make a _____.

I am going to take inspiration from _____.

It is going to be made from _____

_____

_____

because _____

_____.

Its colour and shape will be _____.

The type of person that will use my product will be _____

_____.

☞ 3 In the table below, write a list of points that you want your product to do and not do. This will form a **specification** for your product.

The product must _____

The product must _____

The product must _____

The product must not _____

The product must not _____

The product must not _____

Activity sheet – Designing your own product

Existing products

To help develop your final idea you are going to look at some existing products that are similar to what you want to design.

☞ 1 Research some products that are similar to the one you want to design. Draw or stick a photo of the product you have researched in the box below.

☞ 2 In the box below draw or stick a photo of a product or a product feature that you might use in your design, such as a handle.

☞ 3 In the box below draw or stick a photo of a completely different product to the one you will be designing, but one that shows a shape, material or colour that you would use.

☞ 4 To the right of your examples, write down what you think of each one. How would you use ideas from them for your own design?

Design your own product

☞ Use the boxes below to draw or write down ideas for your product. Make sure you label your work to explain what you have drawn. Label the materials you could use to make the product. Say what inspired you. Remember to think about its size, shape, and so on.

Design 1

Design 2

Design 3

Design 4

Product design

Activity sheet – Designing your own product

Chosen idea

☞ Decide which design from the Activity sheet, 'Design your own product', is your final idea. Draw it out below on a larger scale to give you a chance to think about how you will make it. Remember to label your work to identify which materials you would use and how you think it could be assembled.

Teacher's notes

Evaluation

Objectives

- To be able to evaluate work throughout a project
- To be able to test work to make sure that it functions correctly
- To identify ways of improving work in the future

Prior knowledge

Students should have completed a piece of work that they need to evaluate and suggest improvements. Alternatively, students could evaluate existing products.

NC links

Key concepts: 1.4 Critical evaluation
Key processes: h
Range and content: a, c, d
Curriculum opportunities: a

Northern Ireland PoS

Designing: h

Scottish attainment targets

Skills in designing and making: reviewing and reporting on tasks: Level B
Developing informed attitudes: respect and care for self and others

Welsh PoS

Skills: Designing 9

Background

This unit will enable students to evaluate their own work through self-assessment and evaluate other students' or designers' work through peer assessment to identify areas to develop.

Starter activity

Question students about things that they like to eat such as breakfast cereal. Ask students to talk about why they like or buy certain types of breakfast cereal. Move the discussion on to something else that students might enjoy (such as games consoles or mobile phones) and continue to ask them questions about these products. Highlight to students that what they have been doing is evaluating these products, which is what this unit is all about.

Resource sheets and Activity sheets

The Resource sheet, 'Evaluation cube', is designed to help students to start asking questions about their own and other people's work. This could be developed further so that students could make up their own cubes and questions, depending on the projects they intend to do.

Students are asked to carry out an assessment of their own and other students' work as it is in progress, in relation to a range of user groups using the Activity sheet, 'User groups'. This activity is designed to encourage students to peer assess other students' work, as well as their own to aid the product's development.

Students are required to test their product to see if it works and to encourage other students to comment on their work using the Activity sheet, 'Testing'.

The Activity sheet, 'Self-evaluation', encourages students to think about their work and how they feel about it. They are required to answer specific questions and then write and answer their own questions to show how well they feel their work went.

Having evaluated their product, students should then identify any changes they could make to their work to improve it using the Activity sheet, 'Further development'. The identified changes could then be drawn out to show an updated product that could be developed as an extension task.

Plenary

Discuss with students that the evaluation process takes place throughout the whole development process of a project in order to create the best piece of work possible. Choose a selection of students' work (or every piece if possible) and encourage students to evaluate the products as a group, suggesting ways in which they can be improved.

Resource sheet – Evaluation

Evaluation cube

Below is a net for a cube that can be cut out and glued together to help you evaluate products. Cut the net out and stick it together. Roll the cube like a dice and answer the question it lands on.

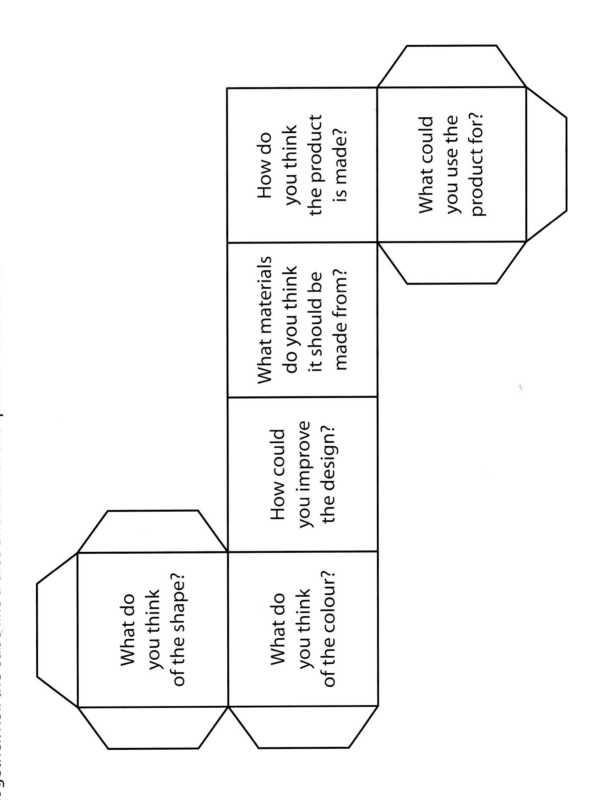

How do you think the product is made?

What could you use the product for?

What materials do you think it should be made from?

How could you improve the design?

What do you think of the shape?

What do you think of the colour?

Product design

Activity sheet – Evaluation

User groups

As your work progresses it is good to see what your classmates think of it. Their comments could help you to improve your work.

☞ 1 In a small group, present your work so far. Write down any feedback that other students give you that could help to improve your work.

☞ 2 In another small group, discuss each others' projects to decide if each product would be suitable for the following user groups. Decide how you could test each product to see if these user groups could use them.

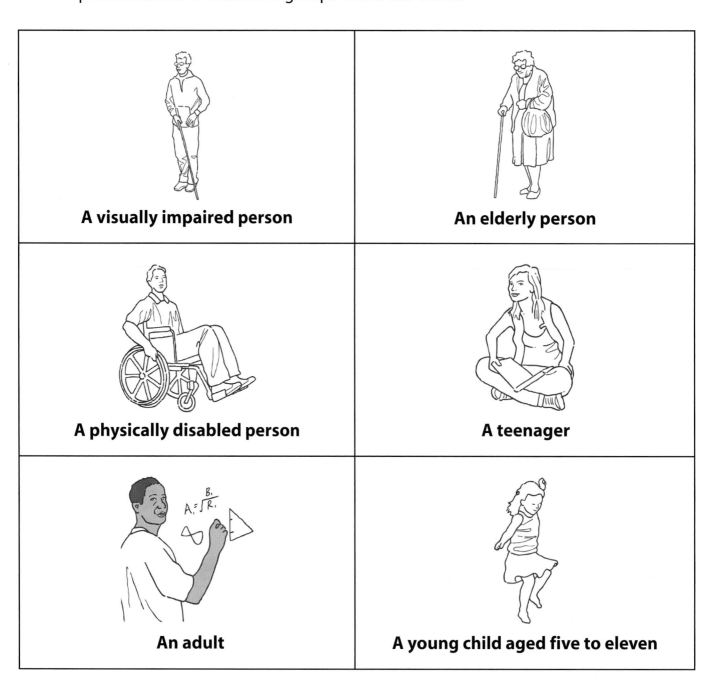

A visually impaired person	An elderly person
A physically disabled person	A teenager
An adult	A young child aged five to eleven

Product design © Folens (copiable page)

Activity sheet – Evaluation

Testing

Once you have made a product you will need to test it to see if it works and to make sure it will do the job it was made to do.

☞ 1 Test your product by making sure it does the job it was made to do.

☞ 2 Take a photo of your product doing its job and glue it into the box below.

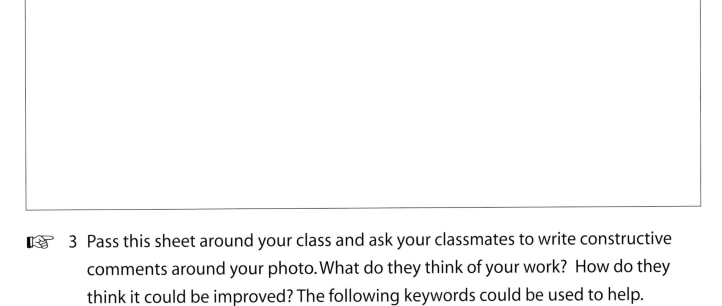

☞ 3 Pass this sheet around your class and ask your classmates to write constructive comments around your photo. What do they think of your work? How do they think it could be improved? The following keywords could be used to help.

Keywords			
• Made from	• Quality	• Idea	• Design
• Works well	• Size	• Colour	• Looks
• Shape	• Weight	• Size	• Easy to use
• User group	• Product	• Perform	

Self-evaluation

☞ 1 To help you evaluate what you think is good about your work, answer the questions below.

Question 1: Name two things that you like about your work and why.

> The best things about my work are:

Question 2: What do you think works well in your design and why?

> The things that work well in my design are:

Question 3: What makes your design better than existing designs of the same product?

> My product is better because:

☞ 2 Now write and answer two of your own questions.

Question 4: _____

Question 5: _____

Activity sheet – Evaluation

Further development

Now that you have finished your project, you will know how hard it was to design and make! Often, once you have finished making something you will think of changes that you would make if you were to make it all over again. For example, could you make your product:

- Look better?
- Work better?
- Easier to use?

Could you change your design to make it:

- Cheaper?
- From more recycled materials?
- More environmentally-friendly?

☞ 1 Fill in the writing frame below to explain your product. You could include things about its size, shape, colour and texture for example.

My product, _____, works _____
_____.

If I was to start the whole project again, I would make the following changes to my work: _____
_____
_____
_____

because _____
_____
_____.

The materials and tools I used to make my product include _____
_____.

I have learnt how to _____
_____ whilst making my product.

☞ 2 On a separate piece of paper, redraw your product with some of the changes you would make to it as you have explained in Task 1.

Assessment sheet – Product design

☞ Tick the boxes in the table below that show what you know or what you can do.

What can I do?	Yes I can	Sometimes I can/I'm not sure	No, I can't do that yet
1 I can say what designs I like and dislike and why.			
2 I know where materials come from and can recognize ones that can be recycled.			
3 I can recognize that products need to be different sizes for different people.			
4 I can name different modern materials.			
5 I can identify different ways that products can be made.			
6 I can model my ideas for new products.			
7 I can draw my own ideas.			
8 I can design my own egg cup and say what is good or bad about my idea.			
9 I can come up with my own ideas for projects.			
10 I can evaluate my own and others' designs, saying what is good and bad about them.			